Fig the Death!

A Play

Stan Cullimore

Illustrated by
Paul Savage

Titles in Full Flight Impact

The Bombed House	Jonny Zucker
Gang of Fire	Jonny Zucker
Big Brother @ School	Jillian Powell
Rollercoaster	Jillian Powell
Monster Planet	David Orme
Danger Mountain	David Orme
Goal Scorers	Jonny Zucker
Basketball	Tony Norman
Fight to the Death! A Play	Stan Cullimore
Stop Talking at the Back and other poems	(ed.) Jonny Zucker

Badger Publishing Limited
Oldmedow Road, Hardwick Industrial Estate,
King's Lynn PE30 4JJ
Telephone: 01438 791037
www.badger-publishing.co.uk

2 4 6 8 10 9 7 5 3 1

Fight to the Death! A Play   ISBN 978 1 85880 385 2

First edition © 2003

This second edition © 2013

Text © Stan Cullimore 2003
Series editing © Jonny Zucker 2003
Complete work © Badger Publishing Limited 2003

Series Editor: Jonny Zucker.
Editor: Paul Martin.
Publisher: David Jamieson.

Cover design: Jain Birchenough.
Cover illustration: Paul Savage.

Fight to the Death!

Stan Cullimore

Contents

Characters

Rob – has lots of ideas

Nick – always asking questions

Sid – a bit strange

Ruth & Zoë – best friends

Roman Woman, Roman Man, Fat Man – ancient Romans

Scene 1 – In the Park

Rob and Nick walk into the park.
Ruth and Zoë are sitting on a bench
with a mobile phone.

Ruth	Hi. What are you doing?
Nick	Nothing much. What are you two doing?
Zoë	Sending text messages.
Nick	Who to?
Ruth	Wouldn't you like to know.
Ruth/Zoë	He he he.

The two boys look at each other and then walk off.

Rob　　(*Hisses*) I've got an idea. Let's go round behind those bushes. Then we can come back and sneak up on the girls.

Nick　　(*Quietly*) And give them a fright. Nice one. That will teach them not to laugh at us!

Rob　　Yes!

The two boys go behind some bushes. When they are out of sight, they turn round. Then they head back towards the girls. Sid is poking around in a hole under a big bush. Rob and Nick almost trip over him.

Sid	Careful!
Nick	What are you doing, Sid?
Sid	Look what I've found in the ground. It's amazing!
Nick	What is it?
Sid	It looks like a really old wine glass.

Rob grabs the glass and stares at it.

Rob   Yeah, you're right! That
            gives me an idea...

Nick   Do you think it's worth any
            money?

Sid   Careful!

*Sid tries to grab the glass from Rob.
The glass slips. It falls to the ground.
CRASH! And breaks into a hundred
little pieces.*

Sid   Now look what you've done.

*Before anyone can reply, the ground
shakes. The three boys fall to the floor.*

Scene 2 – Where is the Park?

Nick	What was that?
Rob	I think I felt the earth move.
Sid	Weird.
Rob	Come on, let's go and give those two a fright!
Sid	Which two?
Nick	Ruth and Zoë.
Rob	They were laughing at us.
Sid	Wait for me.
Nick	Hey, where *is* the park?
Rob	I don't know.
Sid	I think it's gone.
Nick	Where's the bench?
Rob	And the girls.
Sid	I'm lost!
Nick	So am I.

Rob   Look – a house! Let's go and see if anyone's in.

Sid   I've never seen that house before.

Nick Nor have I. Come to think of it, has anyone ever seen a house that *looks* like that before?

Sid   I have.

Rob   You have?

Nick   Where?

Sid   When my Dad took me to an outdoor museum. It showed you how people lived a long time ago.

Nick   What do you mean?

Sid   (*Gulps*) I think that house is an ancient Roman villa.

Rob   (*Laughs*) Right! We've gone back in time to ancient Rome! Get a life, Sid.

The three boys walk over to the house. A woman comes out of the house. She is wearing strange clothes. She smiles at the boys and lifts her hand.

Woman   Salve!

Nick   What?

Sid	I think she said "hello".
Rob	It didn't sound like "hello".
	It sounded like "salve".
Sid	It's a Latin word.
Nick	What's Latin?
Sid	It's what people spoke in ancient Rome.

Rob	You're mad! So is she. She must belong to one of those groups who pretend they live in the old days.
Nick	I don't know, Rob. Something strange is going on. What do you think, Sid?
Sid	Well, I haven't got a signal on my mobile. That's never happened in the park before.
Rob	Who cares? I'm off.
Nick	Where're you going?
Rob	To find something to eat. There must be a burger place around here somewhere.

Scene 3 – Stranger in the Woods

Rob walks off. Nick and Sid follow him. They find a track through the trees. They start to walk along it.

Nick   What's that noise?

Rob   Sounds like someone is coming this way.

Sid   And it sounds like they've got horses with them.

Rob   But no one has horses round here.

Nick   We're in the middle of a town!

Sid   This is all very weird.

*Two horses appear. They are pulling a
big wooden cart. There's a man sitting
on the cart. He stops by the boys.*

Man   Salve!

Rob   He's doing it now.

Nick   What?

Rob   Talking Latin! And he's
            dressed like a Roman.

*The man smiles and holds up a bottle.
He pretends to drink from it. He hands
the bottle to Rob.*

Rob   I am a bit thirsty. Thanks.

Rob sniffs the bottle and takes a drink.

Rob	Not bad. Not bad at all. Here, Nick, have some.
Nick	Thanks. It's very nice. Here, Sid, have some.
Sid	I'm not sure about this.
Nick	Go on. Try it. It's nice.
Sid	OK... It tastes like some sort of wine.
Rob	I feel sleepy.

Rob falls over. He stands up and holds onto the cart.

Nick	Do you feel funny?
Rob	I do.
Sid	I think there was something in that drink.

The three boys fall to the ground
and fall fast asleep.

Man   Ha ha ha ha ha!

The man lifts all three boys onto the
back of the cart and sets off.

Scene 4 – In Trouble

The boys wake up to find themselves in a small room. There are bars over the windows and door.

Nick   Where are we?

Sid   It looks like some kind of prison.

Rob   This is not good. This is really not good.

Nick   Sid, do you really think it's possible to travel back in time?

Sid   As far as I can make out – that's exactly what's happened.

Nick   You think we've travelled back in time?

19

Sid	Yes. I think we're in ancient Rome!
Rob	Hey, look outside. There's the guy who gave us that stuff to drink.
Nick	The rat! He must have put us in here.
Sid	Hang on. Be quiet a minute.
Nick	Why?
Sid	I want to hear what he's saying.

The boys listen in silence for a few moments.

Rob	I can't understand what he's saying.
Sid	He's speaking Latin. Sshh!

The man stops talking. He walks off.

Sid goes pale.

Rob   What's wrong with you, Sid?

Sid   We're in trouble. Big trouble.

Nick   What do you mean?

Sid   Have you ever seen that film, *Gladiator*?

Nick   The one where they have to fight to the death?

Rob   It's a great film.

Sid   I'm sure it is. But they want us to do it for real!

Scene 5 – Fight to the Death!

At that moment, the Roman man opens the prison door. He pushes the boys through a tunnel. The boys go through a gate. They find themselves in a big, open arena with a large crowd staring down at them.

Nick   But I don't want to fight.

Rob   Nor do I.

Nick   Do you want to fight, Sid?

Sid   No, but I don't think we get much choice. Look!

Rob and Nick look around.

Nick   Where's the person we have to fight?

Sid   It's not a person.

Rob   What!

Sid   We have to fight that lion.

Nick/Rob WHAT LION?

*Sid points to the other side of the ring.
A gate has opened. A lion walks out
into the arena.*

Sid   That one.

Nick   (*Gulps*) That's not one
            lion – it's two lions.

Another lion walks out into the arena.

Rob   Make that three lions.

Nick   Am I the only one that thinks
            we're in BIG trouble?

Sid   This time travel stuff is not as
            much fun as I thought it
            would be. Look – they're
            licking their lips.

Rob   Stay still. Maybe they won't
            be able to see us.

Sid   They don't need to see us.
            They can smell us!

Rob   We can't fight lions.

Nick   How about if we just run
            away from them?

Sid   No. There's only one thing
            we can do.

Nick   What's that?

Sid   This.

Sid starts to climb over the high gate the boys have just come through.

Nick   That's a good idea isn't it, Rob?

Nick looks for Rob. He is climbing up the gate after Sid.

Nick   Wait for me!

The boys climb over the gate. The crowd starts to boo.

Nick   Now what do we do, Sid?

Sid   Stay away from him!

Sid points to the Roman man.

He pokes the boys with a spear.

Sid   Hey!

Nick   What are you doing, mate?

Rob   Stop it!

Nick   He is NOT a very nice man.

Rob   I hate him.

Sid   Let's try in here.

Sid opens a door in the wall.

The other two boys follow him.

Sid   This is more like it.

Nick   Where are we?

Sid   I don't know. But I do know that there aren't any lions in here.

Scene 6 – Now What?

They are standing in a small room with a fat man who is laughing and pointing at them.

Nick   See what he's got?

Rob   It's a glass.

Sid   And it's just like the one I found in the ground.

Rob   I've got an idea.

Nick   What is it?

Rob   We have to get that glass away from him.

Sid and Nick run forward. They grab the fat man.

Fat Man	Quo! (*Grunting noises*)
Rob	Give me your glass!
Fat Man	(*More grunting noises*)
Sid	He doesn't understand what you're saying.
Nick	Why don't you just grab it?

Rob grabs the glass from the fat man.

Nick   Now what?

Rob   The last time I dropped a
glass like this – we went
back in time.
So if I drop this glass…

Sid   … it might just take us
forward to our own time.

Rob   Ready?

Nick   It will never work.

*The fat man waddles out of the room.
He shouts something in Latin as he
leaves.*

Sid   Hurry up!

Nick   Why?

Sid   That man has just called the
guards. He wants them to
kill us.

Rob   Here goes!

Rob drops the glass. It falls to the ground. CRASH! And breaks into a hundred little pieces.

Nick   It didn't work! I knew it
           wouldn't.
Sid   Oh!
Nick   Now what do we...?

The ground shakes and the boys fall to the floor.

Scene 7 – The Longest Five Minutes of my life!

The boys stand up. They are in the park. A phone bleeps.

Sid   I've got a text message – it's from Ruth.

Ruth and Zoë appear from behind a tree.

Ruth	There you are.
Zoë	Where have you been hiding for the last five minutes?

The boys look at each other.

Sid	You wouldn't believe us if we told you.
Rob	Really, you wouldn't!
Nick	We were only gone for five minutes?
Ruth	Yes.
Zoë	Why do you ask?
Nick	Because it was the longest five minutes of my life!

THE END